How this curriculum is designed

This curriculum is designed to guide you through a sequence of scenarios that relate to a common topic in mathematics. As you progress through the scenarios, use the approach listed below.

Step 1: Try. Do the scenario on your own.

Step 2: Check. Look at the answer key. It may match or relate to your result. It may teach you something new. It may show you that you need guidance from someone else.

Step 3: Edit. Find and fix your mistakes if you can. Seek guidance, if needed.

After Step 3, advance to the next scenario and do Step 1 again.

Advice from students who have used this curriculum

"The answer key is there to help you. Use it."

"Check the answer key after every scenario."

"Try to find connections between different scenarios."

"Focus on each scenario and try to understand how it connects to the main topic."

"Read the explanations between problems or sets of problems because everything is connected and the information will still apply in 2 problems or 20 problems."

"If you have a question, go back to previous scenarios because there are steps that build up to where you are."

Contents

D1511460

Review multiplying polynomials

In later scenarios, you will eventually learn about a topic known as factoring. However, you first need to review how multiplying polynomials forms new polynomials.

1. Given the areas of the rectangles below, determine the lengths of a, b, c and d.

2. The area of the entire rectangle above can be expressed as 63 cm². If the area is written as the base times the height, it can be expressed as $(21 \cdot 3)$ cm². We'll be looking more closely at this later. Given the areas of the rectangles below, determine the lengths of a, b, and c.

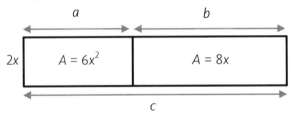

The area of the entire rectangle above can be expressed as $6x^2 + 8x$. If the area is written as the base times the height, it can be expressed as $(3x+4)(2x)$ or $2x(3x+4)$. The base is a binomial, 3x + 4, and the height is a monomial, 2x, to review some vocabulary from earlier lessons.

3. Multiply each expression.

    a. $x(x+2)$ b. $3x(7x-5)$ c. $-4x(2x^2-x-6)$

4. Rewrite each expression as the product of a monomial and a binomial. How can you be sure that your product is a correctly rewritten form of the original expression?

    a. $5x^2-20x$ b. $6y^2+15y$

5. What are the values of a, b, and c, in the rectangle shown? Two of the values are side lengths, and the other value is the area of the smaller rectangle.

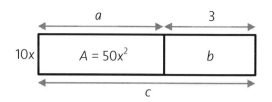

6. Draw a rectangle that has the following area. Label the length of the base and height.

    a. $11x + 33$

    b. $y^2 + y$

7. Rewrite each of the areas in the previous scenario as the product of a monomial and a binomial.

A brief lesson on vocabulary: when you rewrite an expression as the product of two other expressions, as in the previous scenario, the two expressions are called factors. In this context, the word *factor* is a noun. Additionally, the process of rewriting an expression as the product of its factors is often referred to as factoring. In another context, then, the word *factor* is a verb.

8. Write each polynomial as the product of two factors.

    a. $7x + 7$

    b. $10x^2 - 35x + 5$

9. Factor each polynomial.

    a. $3x^2 - 6x - 5$

    b. $8x^3 + 16x^2 + 12x$

Identifying a common factor can lead to different opinions. Consider the polynomial $8x^3 + 20x^2 + 12x$. The three terms of this trinomial share 2 as a common factor, as well as 4 and 4x. In situations like this, it is typical to identify 4x as the greatest common factor (GCF).

10. The terms in the expression below have many factors in common. Identify all of the common factors of the terms in each expression.

    a. $15x^3 + 30x^2 + 45x$

    b. $90x^3 - 30x^2 + 20x^4$

11. Identify the <u>greatest</u> common factor of each expression in the previous scenario.

12. Factor each polynomial below by writing it as the product of a monomial and a remaining polynomial. The monomial should be the greatest common factor of the original polynomial.

    a. $2x^2 + 2x$ b. $12x^3 + 30x^2 - 24x$ c. $16x^4 - 80x^3 - 40x^2$

13. Factor the trinomial $18x^4 + 60x^3 - 30x^2$.

14. A rectangle is divided into 4 smaller rectangles as shown. Calculate the area of each of the smaller rectangles. Write the area of each smaller rectangle inside the space of that rectangle.

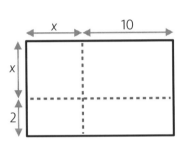

15. Consider the rectangle below. The areas of 3 of the sections are shown in those sections.

    a. Determine the area of the missing section below.

    b. Determine the area of the entire rectangle.

16. Consider the rectangle shown below.

    a. Determine the expression for the area of the entire rectangle.

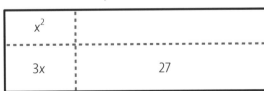

    b. Write the area as the product of its base and height, or (base)(height).

Notes

Writing a trinomial as a product of two binomials

17. In earlier lessons, you learned how to multiply binomials. Bring your mind back to that topic by multiplying the following binomials. Notice how the result relates to the original binomials.

   a. $(x+2)(x-7)$ b. $(x-6)(x+6)$ c. $(x-3)^2$

18. Look at your work for the 3 multiplication scenarios in the previous scenario. Could you do that work in reverse? If you started with your final expression, could you work backwards to figure out the two binomials that you multiplied to make that expression? Try to do that with the following expressions. Write each expression as the product of two binomials.

   a. x^2-2x-3 b. x^2-25 c. $x^2-8x+16$

19. What value of A makes the two expressions equivalent?

   a. $x^2+Ax-18$ and $(x+6)(x-3)$

   b. $x^2+Ax-121$ and $(x+11)(x-11)$

   c. $x^2+Axy+9y^2$ and $(x-3y)^2$

20. It may be helpful to go through the mental cycle of multiplying binomials again. As before, multiply the following binomials. Try to make connections between your final expression and the original binomials that you multiplied.

   a. $(x+3)(x-5)$ b. $(x-7)(x+7)$ c. $(x+2y)^2$

21. Once again, try to work backwards to write each expression as the product of two binomials.

   a. $x^2+7x+10$ b. x^2-y^2 c. $y^2-12y+36$

The single most important mental activity involved in factoring is the process of multiplying your factors together to check your answer.

22. Fill in the blank to make each expression equal to the factors written below the expression.

a.
$$x^2 + \underline{\quad} x - 21$$
$$(x+7)(x-3)$$

b.
$$x^2 + \underline{\quad} x - 6$$
$$(x-6)(x+1)$$

c.
$$x^2 - 14x + 24$$
$$(x + \underline{\quad})(x-2)$$

23. Multiply the expressions below to find an equivalent expression without parentheses.

$$4(x+1)(x+3)$$

24. When you try to multiply the expressions above, it may be confusing to know how to proceed with the "4" to the left of the first binomial. You may find it easier to first multiply the binomials before distributing the "4", but you can also start by distributing the "4" to the first binomial. Try a third option. Distribute the "4" to both of the binomials and then multiply the binomials. Write down your simplified result to see if it matches the other two options.

25. Multiply the expressions below to find an equivalent expression without parentheses.

$$-2(x-5)(x+1)$$

26. Fill in the blank to make each expression equal to the factors written below the expression.

a.
$$2x^2 + \underline{\quad} x - 4$$
$$2(x-2)(x+1)$$

b.
$$x^3 + \underline{\quad} x^2 - 10x$$
$$x(x+2)(x-5)$$

c.
$$-x^2 - 3x + 18$$
$$-(x + \underline{\quad})(x+6)$$

27. For the trinomial $2x^2 - 10x - 12$, which factorization is correct?

$$2(x-3)(x+2) \quad \text{or} \quad 2(x-3)(x-2)$$

28. Each trinomial below has been factored but the plus or minus signs are missing. Fill in either a plus sign (+) or a minus sign (−) to make the factors correct.

a.
$$x^2 + 7x + 10$$
$$(x \quad 2)(x \quad 5)$$

b.
$$x^2 + 8x + 7$$
$$(x \quad 7)(x \quad 1)$$

c.
$$x^2 + 35x + 124$$
$$(x \quad 4)(x \quad 31)$$

29. Each trinomial below has been factored but some of the signs and numbers are missing. Fill in any missing details to make the factors correct.

a.
$$x^2 + 7x - 18$$
$$\left(x \quad 2\right)\left(x \quad 9\right)$$

b.
$$x^2 - 5x - 6$$
$$\left(x \quad 6\right)\left(x \quad 1\right)$$

c.
$$x^2 + 27x - 160$$
$$\left(x \quad 5\right)\left(x \quad 32\right)$$

30. Write each trinomial as the product of two binomials. This is also called <u>factoring</u> the trinomial.

a. $x^2 + 3x + 2$
b. $x^2 - 3x + 2$
c. $x^2 - x - 2$
d. $x^2 + x - 2$

31. Factor each polynomial below by writing it as the product of a monomial and a remaining polynomial. The monomial should be the greatest common factor of the original polynomial.

a. $4x^2 - 20x$
b. $-6x^2 + 18x - 3$
c. $14x^3 - 7x^2 - 35x$

32. Each trinomial below has been factored but some details are missing. Fill in any missing details to make the factors correct.

a.
$$x^2 - 13x + 12$$
$$\left(x \quad 12\right)\left(x \quad 1\right)$$

b.
$$x^2 - 11x + 24$$
$$\left(x \quad 3\right)\left(x \quad 8\right)$$

c.
$$x^2 - 55x + 600$$
$$\left(x \quad 40\right)\left(x \quad 15\right)$$

33. Factor each trinomial. Check your answer by multiplying your factors together. By doing this, you can prove that your factors are correct.

a. $x^2 + 6x - 7$

b. $100x^2 + 600x - 700$

The previous scenario is designed to show you that it helps to start out by *trying* to factor out a GCF from the entire expression. You may not be *able* to factor out a GCF, but if you can, it may help you find additional factors more easily.

34. Factor each trinomial below.

a. $x^5 + 6x^4 - 7x^3$
b. $-2x^2 - 12x + 14$
c. $-3x^2 - 18x + 21$

35. Factor the following trinomials. Verify that your factors are correct by multiplying them together.

  a. $2x^2 + 4x - 6$

  b. $-3x^2 - 21x - 30$

36. Factor the trinomial $3x^2 + 4x - 7$.

Factoring the trinomial in the previous scenario can be challenging. It is easier to factor a trinomial when the leading coefficient is 1 (as in $1x^2$, or simply x^2). If the leading coefficient is any number other than 1, you need to pay attention to that coefficient and carefully check your factors.

37. Identify the leading coefficient in each trinomial. Rewrite each trinomial in Standard Form.

  a. $1 + 3x^2 - x$

  b. $2x + x^2 - 9$

  c. $3 - 8x - x^2$

38. Factor the following trinomials. Check your answer by multiplying your factors together.

  a. $11x + 5 + 2x^2$

  b. $5 + 16x + 3x^2$

  c. $4x^2 + 4x - 15$

39. What value of B makes the two expressions equivalent?

  a. $2x^2 + Bx - 10$ and $(2x - 5)(x + 2)$

  b. $3x^2 + Bx + 7$ and $(x - 7)(3x - 1)$

  c. $10x^2 + Bx - 18$ and $2(5x + 9)(x - 1)$

40. Factor the following trinomials. Check your answer by multiplying your factors together.

  a. $7x - 6 + 3x^2$

  b. $7 + 4x^2 - 16x$

  c. $-5x^2 + 12 - 17x$

At this point, there isn't much more to learn about factoring. In order to strengthen your long-term understanding of this topic, though, we will continue to look more closely at factoring and try to sort out some of the patterns that may help you factor expressions more quickly.

41. Factor the following trinomials. Check your answer by multiplying your factors together. By doing this, you can prove that your factors are correct.

    a. $2x^2 - x - 6$

    b. $20x^2 - 10x - 60$

Once again, the previous scenario is designed to show you that it helps to start out by *trying* to factor out a GCF from the entire expression. You may not be *able* to factor out a GCF, but if you can, it may help you find additional factors more easily.

42. Factor each trinomial below.

    a. $2x^3 - x^2 - 6x$

    b. $-6x^2 + 3x + 18$

    c. $30 + 5x - 10x^2$

43. Explain why $(x-3)(x-2)$ cannot be the factorization of $x^2 - 5x - 6$.

44. Layla claims to know the factors for $2x^2 + 16x - 40$. Her factorization is written down as $(2x-4)(x+10)$. Is there another way to factor the original trinomial?

Notes

Factoring a difference of two squares

45. Factor the following expressions. Check your answer by multiplying your factors together.

    a. $x^2 + 0x - 4$ b. $x^2 + 0x - 9$ c. $16 + 0x - x^2$

46. Factor the following expressions. Check your answer by multiplying your factors together.

    a. $25 + 0x - x^2$ b. $x^2 - 49$ c. $81 - x^2$

47. Factor the following expressions. Check your answer by multiplying your factors together.

    a. $x^2 - 100$ b. $y^2 - 25$ c. $m^2 - 400$

48. Factor the following expressions. Check your answer by multiplying your factors together.

    a. $2x^2 - 8$ b. $2x^2 - 18$ c. $48 - 3x^2$

49. Factor the following expressions. Check your answer by multiplying your factors together.

    a. $75 - 3x^2$ b. $x^3 - 49x$ c. $-2x^2 + 72$

50. If $x^2 - 36$ can be factored as $(x+6)(x-6)$, how can $x^2 + 36$ be factored?

51. Factor the following expressions.

    a. $4x^2 - 49$

    b. $16x^2 - 25y^2$

52. Factor the following expressions as much as you can.

    a. $x^4 - 81$

    b. $x^4 - 1$

When a polynomial has a structure of $A^2 - B^2$, this structure is known as a difference of two squares. When it has this structure, its factors are the two binomials: $(A + B)(A - B)$. Notice that in the previous scenario, the polynomials factored once and then the remaining expressions could be factored again.

53. Factor the expression $x^8 - 1$ as much as you can.

Notes

Factoring perfect square trinomials

54. Factor the following trinomials. Check your answer by multiplying your factors together.

    a. x^2+2x+1 b. x^2-4x+4 c. x^2-6x+9

55. Factor the following trinomials. Check your answer by multiplying your factors together.

    a. $4x^2+20x+25$ b. $1-10x+25x^2$ c. $36-36x+9x^2$

56. What pattern do you notice in the previous two scenarios?

57. Factor the following trinomials.

    a. $y^2-2xy+x^2$ b. $4x^2-28xy+49y^2$

58. Factor the following trinomials.

    a. $-28x+2x^2+98$ b. $-x^3-18x^2-81x$ c. $-x^2+10xy-25y^2$

When you factor a trinomial and it has two factors that are exactly the same, it is called a <u>perfect square trinomial</u>. Just as 16 is a perfect square because it can be written as 4^2, a trinomial is a perfect square if it can be written as a binomial squared.

59. One type of perfect square trinomial will always factor into $\left(A+B\right)\left(A+B\right)$ or $\left(A+B\right)^2$. Multiply these factors back together to see the original trinomial.

60. A perfect square trinomial may also sometimes factor into $\left(A-B\right)\left(A-B\right)$ or $\left(A-B\right)^2$. Multiply these factors back together to see the original trinomial.

61. Factor the expression $A^2 - 20AB + 100B^2$.

62. Explain why $(x-15)(x-4)$ cannot be the factorization of $2x^2 - 19x + 60$.

63. Your classmate claims to have the factors for $x^3 - 7x^2 - 18x$. His factorization is written down as $(x^2 - 9x)(x+2)$. Is there another way to factor the original trinomial?

64. Consider the trinomial $25 - 10x + x^2$. If you factor it as $(5-x)^2$, but I factor it as $(x-5)^2$, how can we figure out whose factors are correct?

65. Factor the following trinomials.

    a. $A^2 + 2AB + B^2$ b. $A^2 - 2AB + B^2$ c. $-30x + 9x^2 + 25$

66. Explain how to determine if a trinomial is a perfect square trinomial.

Notes

Using factoring to solve equations

Let's take a break from factoring to consider some scenarios that contain polynomials like the ones we have been working with so far.

67. Suppose you attempt a basketball foul shot. The path of the ball as it travels through the air is modeled by the equation $H=-16t^2+20t+6$, where H is the height of the ball, measured in feet, t seconds after it leaves your hand. What is the height of the ball at the exact moment the ball is released?

68. In the previous scenario, suppose the shot misses the basket completely and hits the ground below the basket. How long after the ball is released does it hit the ground? Try to set up an equation that would help you answer this question. If this is confusing, keep reading.

When the ball hits the ground, its height is 0. In the equation $H=-16t^2+20t+6$, if you replace H with 0, the equation becomes $0=-16t^2+20t+6$. You can try to isolate "t" in this equation, but you probably do not know how to solve this type of equation yet.

In the next scenarios, you will learn about equations that involve w^2, t^2, n^2, or even x^2. First, consider this: When you solve an equation like $2x - 6 = 17$, the variable appears in only one term. As a result, you can undo the operations to isolate the variable x. You can add 6 to undo the subtracted 6 and you can divide by 2 to undo the multiplied 2. Once you understand how to undo every operation, you can <u>always</u> isolate x in this type of equation.

69. Now consider an equation like $x^2+5x=-6$.

    a. You can try to combine the two terms containing "x" but they are not **like** terms.

    b. If you undo the multiplied 5 in "$5x$" by dividing both sides by "5" you will end up with $\dfrac{x^2}{5}+x=\dfrac{-6}{5}$. This looks even more confusing.

    c. You can factor out an x to get $x(x+5)=-6$ and then divide both sides by $(x + 5)$, but the equation becomes $x=\dfrac{-6}{x+5}$, which also looks very confusing.

You can keep trying to isolate the variable to solve the equation, but you need a new strategy.

70. Start by moving all of the terms to the left side of the equation, which yields $x^2+5x+6=0$. Now put your factoring practice to work and rewrite the trinomial as the product of two factors.

71. When the trinomial is factored, the equation becomes $(x+3)(x+2)=0$. As a reminder, the goal is to find all possible values of x that make the equation true. Spend some time trying out different numbers until you find a number that makes the left side of the equation equal 0.

72. If it is difficult for you to find numbers that make the previous equation equal 0, it is easier if you think about each factor separately. The expression $(x+3)(x+2)$ has a value of "0" if $x+3=0$ or if $x+2=0$. If you solve each equation separately, $x = -3$ or $x = -2$.

   a. The expression $(x-3)(x-4)$ has a value of "0" if _____ $=0$ or if _____ $=0$.

   b. The expression $(x+2)(x+5)$ is equal to "0" if _____ $=0$ or if _____ $=0$.

   c. The equation $(3x-1)(2x+3)=0$ is true if _____ $=0$ or if _____ $=0$.

73. Solve this puzzle: Anna is thinking of two numbers. When she multiplies the numbers together, their product is zero. One of the numbers is 7. What is the other number?

74. Here is another puzzle for you. There are two numbers A and B. A is 3 more than B. When you multiply these numbers together, their product is zero. What are the values of A and B?

75. What value of x makes each equation true?

   a. $x-1=0$
   b. $0=x+1$
   c. $x-7=0$
   d. $0=x+3$

76. What x-value makes each equation true?

   a. $4(x-1)=0$
   b. $3(x+2)=0$
   c. $2(x+5)=0$

77. What x-values make each equation true?

   a. $(x-2)(x+3)=0$
   b. $(x+7)(x-1)=0$
   c. $(x-4)(x-5)=0$

78. In the scenarios above, the factors have a product of 0. Why does this make it possible to determine values of x that make each equation true?

79. The equation $(A)(B)=0$ is true if $A = 0$. It is also true if $B = 0$. Suppose, instead that $(A)(B)=1$. What values of A and B make this statement true?

80. Solve the equation $(x-2)(x+3)=1$ by setting both factors equal to 1. Check your solutions to see if either one makes the original equation true.

81. Which equation is easier to solve? Why is this?

Equation 1: $(x-1)(x-2)=12$ Equation 2: $(x-1)(x-2)=0$

82. What x-value makes each equation true?

a. $(x+1)(x+3)=0$ b. $(x+6)(x+4)=0$ c. $(x-8)(x+2)=0$

83. Solve the following equations.

a. $x^2+4x+3=0$ b. $x^2+10x+24=0$ c. $x^2-6x-16=0$

84. Solve the equation $x^2-7x+10=0$.

85. Solve the equation $x^2-3x=70$.

86. Solve the equation $x^2+36=12x$.

87. Solve the equation $(x-4)(x-3)=2$.

88. What x-value makes each equation true?

    a. $2x-4=0$ b. $3x+6=0$ c. $4x-1=0$ d. $5x+3=0$

89. What x-value makes each equation true?

    a. $2(3x-2)=0$ b. $5(6x+1)=0$ c. $2(2x-5)=0$

90. What values of x make each equation true?

    a. $(6x-1)(2x-1)=0$ b. $(3x+2)(3x-2)=0$ c. $(3x+4)(5x-1)=0$

91. What values of x make each equation true?

    a. $(2x-3)(x-2)=0$ b. $(2x-5)(2x-5)=0$ c. $(3x+5)(x-1)=0$

92. Solve the following equations.

    a. $2x^2-7x+6=0$ b. $4x^2-20x+25=0$ c. $3x^2+2x-5=0$

93. Solve the equation $5x^2 - 9x - 2 = 0$.

94. Solve the equation $25x^2 + 4 = 20x$.

95. Solve the equation $6x^2 + 11x = 10$.

96. The next group of equations may seem confusing because they have a slightly different structure than the previous ones that you have seen so far. What values of x make each equation true?

a. $x(x-4) = 0$

b. $x(x+7) = 0$

c. $2x(4x-1) = 0$

97. In each of the previous three equations, one of the solutions is 0. Why does this occur?

98. Solve the following equations.

a. $x^2 - 8x = 0$

b. $2x^2 + 6x = 0$

c. $5x^3 - 30x^2 = 0$

99. What values of x make each equation true?

a. $2x^2(x+9) = 0$

b. $4x^3(x-10) = 0$

★c. $5x(x^2-4) = 0$

100. Solve the following equations in two different ways. For the first approach, factor as you have learned to do in the previous scenarios. For the second approach, divide both sides by x and then proceed with factoring. What do you notice?

    a. $x^2 = 3x$ b. $x^3 - 8x^2 + 12x = 0$

101. Explain how you would start to solve the equation $x(x-4) = 5$.

102. Solve the following equations.

    a. $2x^3 - 10x^2 + 12x = 0$ b. $4x^3 = 100x$

103. Solve the following equations.

    a. $-6x^2 + 54x + 60 = 0$ b. $-9x^2 + 36 = 0$

104. Solve each of the following equations. These equations appeared in previous scenarios.

    a. $0 = -16t^2 + 20t + 6$ b. $(n+2)^2 = 324$

105. Solve the equation $(x+3)(x+2)=2$. Check your solutions.

106. Can you solve the equation $(x+3)(3x+5)=7$ by letting $(x+3)=7$ and $(3x+5)=7$? If so, do this and check your results.

107. Solve the equation $(2x+1)(4x-1)=14$.

108. Solve the equation $2x(x-1)=12$.

109. How many solutions does the equation have?

$$x^3 + x = 2x^2$$

Notes

Scenarios that involve factoring

110. The area of the entire rectangle below is 48 square units. What is the value of x?

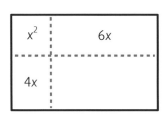

111. Although you missed the net on your earlier foul shot, you maintain your confidence and pick up the ball again, this time to attempt a half court shot. On this shot attempt, the path of the ball is modeled by the equation $y = -16t^2 + 46t + 6$, where y is the height of the ball, measured in feet, t seconds after its release.

    a. What is the height of the ball after 1 second?

    b. Suppose the shot misses the basket completely again and hits the ground below the basket. How long was the ball in the air before it hit the ground this time?

    ★c. How many seconds after its release is the ball 25 feet above the ground?

112. The area of the rectangle shown is 24 cm^2.

    a. What is the value of x?

    b. What is the perimeter of the rectangle?

113. ★If the area of the rectangle in the previous scenario is $9\frac{3}{4}$ cm^2, what are its dimensions? This is easier to figure out if you can find a way to eliminate the fractions.

114. You want to build a rectangular frame with a length that is 8 inches more than its width. If the side lengths must be integers and the area of the frame is 105 in^2, what are the dimensions of the frame?

115. The area of the triangle shown is 35 cm^2. What is the length of the base of the triangle?

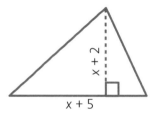

116. If the area of a triangle is 9 cm^2 and its height is 5 cm shorter than twice the length of its base, what are the dimensions of the triangle?

117. In the progression below, the 1st Figure contains 5 tiles and the 2nd Figure contains 10 tiles. Follow the pattern below and see if you can apply your algebraic fluency to this new scenario.

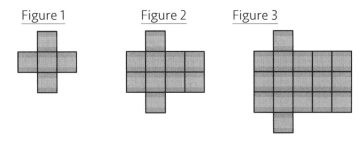

Figure 1   Figure 2   Figure 3

        a. How many tiles will be in the 4th Figure?

        b. How many tiles will be in the nth Figure?

        ★c. Which Figure will contain 122 tiles? Answer this by creating and solving an equation.

118. Solve the following equations.

        a. $3x - 5 = 4 + 2x$
        b. $\dfrac{x-8}{3} = 5$
        c. $\dfrac{x}{3} - 4 = 2$

119. Solve the following equations.

        a. $x^2 - 8x = 0$
        b. $2x^3 - 50x = 0$
        c. $3x^2 - 5 = 2x$

There are many types of equations that you have learned how to solve (and more to come). Equations like $3x - 5 = 8$ and $-2x + 3 = x$ usually have one solution and they are known as <u>linear</u> equations. Linear equations can be rearranged to look like $Ax + B = 0$. The equations that you have been learning about in recent scenarios look like $x^2 + 3x + 2 = 0$ and $x^2 + 5x = 6$. These equations are called <u>quadratic</u> equations and they can be rearranged to look like $Ax^2 + Bx + C = 0$.

120. Circle the equations that are quadratic.

     a. $9x^2 - 2x + 3 = 0$ b. $x^2 - 5 = 0$ c. $x^2 = 9$ d. $3x - 5 = 2x$

121. The two solutions to a quadratic equation have a sum of 5 and a product of 6. Write down the equation in the form $Ax^2 + Bx + C = 0$.

122. Determine the value of x that makes the shaded region have an area of 21 square units.

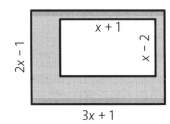

Notes

Using factoring to simplify fractions

123. Simplify each of the following fractions.

    a. $\dfrac{1 \cdot 5}{2 \cdot 5}$ b. $\dfrac{6 \cdot 2}{5 \cdot 6}$ c. $\dfrac{2x}{5x}$ d. $\dfrac{10A}{40A}$

124. Simplify each of the following fractions.

    a. $\dfrac{2(x-1)}{3(x-1)}$ b. $\dfrac{(x+5)(x+2)}{(x+3)(x+2)}$ c. $\dfrac{3x+6}{5x+10}$

125. In the previous scenario, the last fraction can only be simplified after you factor the numerator and denominator. After factoring, it becomes clear that there are identical factors in the numerator and denominator, which create a disguised form of 1. Use this strategy of factoring to simplify the following fraction.

$$\frac{x^2+3x+2}{x^2+6x+8}$$

126. Simplify each fraction by cancelling out disguised forms of 1.

    a. $\dfrac{x^2-9}{x^2-2x-15}$ b. $\dfrac{3x^2-12}{x^2+7x-18}$

127. ★Simplify the following fraction: $\dfrac{8x^2-24x+18}{4x^2+10x-24}$.

Notes

Introduction to graphing parabolas

128. If you graph the equation $y = -x + 4$, what is the shape of your graph? If it is helpful, use the T-chart below to help you find points that are part of the graph. Plot at least 4 points.

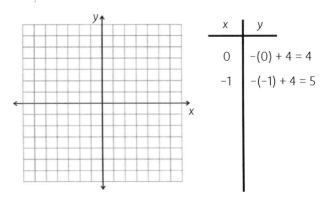

x	y
0	$-(0) + 4 = 4$
−1	$-(-1) + 4 = 5$

129. When you graph all of the ordered pairs represented by the equation $y = x^2 - 4$, the shape of the graph is... actually, maybe you can figure out the shape of the graph. Use what you know about graphing equations to create a graph of this equation. A T-chart is started to help guide you.

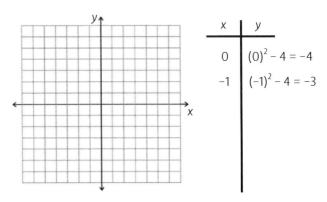

x	y
0	$(0)^2 - 4 = -4$
−1	$(-1)^2 - 4 = -3$

The graph in the previous scenario has a curved shape that makes it very different than linear graphs. In mathematics, there is a technical name for practically everything. This specially curved graph is called a parabola (puh-RA-buh-luh). Additionally, while the structure $y = -x + 4$ is called a linear equation, the structure $y = x^2 - 4$ is called a quadratic equation.

130. Graph the equation $y = x^2 + 2x - 2$.

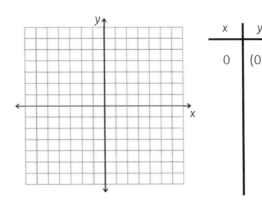

x	y
0	$(0)^2 + 2(0) - 2 = -2$

131. Consider the parabola to the right.

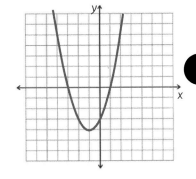

    a. Find a point with a y-value of 0. What is the x-value?

    b. Find a point with an x-value of 2. What is the y-value?

    ★c. Which point on the parabola has a y-value of –5?

132. Determine the x-value(s) for which the equation $y=-2x^2+9x-10$ has a y-value of

    a. 0

    b. –3

133. Identify any x- and y-intercepts for each of the following equations.

    a. $4x-7y=-14$

    b. $y=-6x^2+7x+5$

134. ★Identify any x- and y-intercepts for each of the following equations.

    a. $x^2+y=-9$

    b. $y=25-20x+4x^2$

135. Identify the x- and y-intercepts of the following equation. Then, graph the equation to verify the accuracy of your intercepts.

$$y = x^2 - 4x$$

136. Draw a <u>very basic</u> sketch of a parabola that has each of the following characteristics.

 a. two x-intercepts

 b. one x-intercept

 c. no x-intercepts

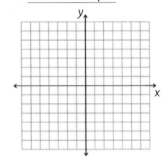

137. Part of a parabola is shown below. Even though you do not have the equation for the parabola, use what you have learned so far to plot more points that are on the parabola. Use those points to finish drawing the parabola.

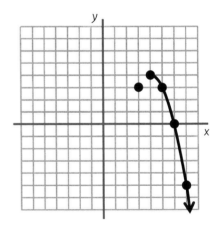

138. Using the grid, draw rectangles that have a perimeter of 24 inches. Draw as many different rectangles as you can discover. The only requirement is that each one must have a perimeter of 24 inches. Mark the length and width of each rectangle in the T-chart to the right of the grid.

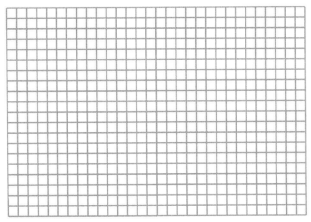

width | length

139. Calculate the area of each rectangle that you drew in the previous scenario. In the table shown, write the width and area measurements. Include more values in the table if you find more widths.

Width											
Area											

140. In the graph shown, plot the data points from your table, with width on the horizontal axis and area on the vertical axis. Try to plot at least 10 points.

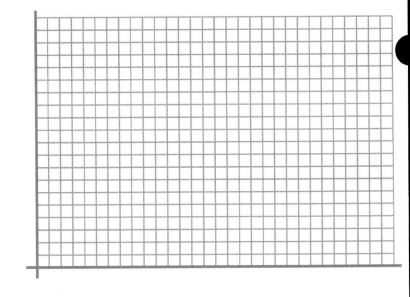

141. A rectangle has a perimeter of 24 inches.

a. What is the length of the rectangle if its width is 4.5 inches? What is its area?

b. What is the length of the rectangle if its width is w?

c. What is the area of the rectangle if its width is w?

Notes

142. Simplify each expression by eliminating parentheses and using only positive exponents.

a. $\dfrac{10x^{-2}}{12x^{-5}}$

b. $\left(\dfrac{-3x^5}{x^{-3}}\right)^2$

c. $\left(\dfrac{2^{-1}a^5}{b^{-2}}\right)^{-3}$

143. It is often difficult to remember the difference between the area and perimeter of a rectangle. You have worked through several scenarios that involve the area of rectangles. Determine the perimeter of each rectangle shown below.

a.

side length

b.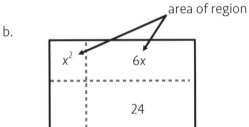

area of region

144. When drivers use the PA Turnpike, they pay a flat fee of $0.25 plus an additional 9.5 cents per mile. How many miles can a driver drive on the turnpike if she wants her toll to be at most $10, rounded to the nearest whole number?

145. A school ordered a new copy machine last year. The bill for the copy machine, which included 7% sales tax, was $868.84. How much did the copy machine cost before taxes were added to the price?

146. Solve each equation.

    a. $-2x+3=3x-7$ b. $\dfrac{1}{2}x-5=-4x+1$

147. What single operation could you perform to solve the equation in 1 step?

    a. $\dfrac{3}{5}x=9$ b. $-\dfrac{2}{3}x=10$

148. Determine the equation of each line shown.

    a.   b.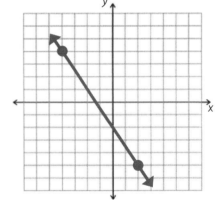

149. Determine the equation of each line shown.

    a.   b.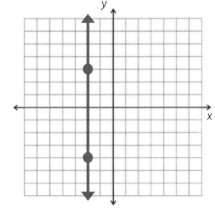

150. In the previous scenario, if you graph the two lines on the same grid, at what ordered pair would the two lines intersect?

1.	a. 5 cm b. 13 cm c. 3 cm d. 21 cm
2.	a. $3x$ b. 4 c. $(3x + 4)$
3.	a. x^2+2x b. $21x^2-15x$ c. $-8x^3+4x^2+24x$
4.	a. $5x(x-4)$ b. $3y(2y+5)$
5.	$a = 5x, b = 30x, c = 5x + 3$
6.	
7.	a. $11(x+3)$ b. $y(y+1)$
8.	a. $7(x+1)$ b. $5\left(2x^2-7x+1\right)$
9.	a. Prime (not factorable) b. $4x\left(2x^2+4x+3\right)$
10.	a. 3, 5, 15, x, 3x, 5x, 15x b. $2,5,10, x,2x,5x,10x, x^2,2x^2,5x^2,10x^2$
11.	a. $15x$ b. $10x^2$
12.	a. $2x(x+1)$ b. $6x(2x^2+5x-4)$ c. $8x^2(2x^2-10x-5)$
13.	$6x^2(3x^2+10x-5)$
14.	
15.	a. $4x$ b. $x^2+10x+24$
16.	a. $x^2+12x+27$ b. $(x+9)(x+3)$
17.	a. $x^2-5x-14$ b. x^2-36 c. x^2-6x+9
18.	a. $(x+1)(x-3)$ b. $(x+5)(x-5)$ c. $(x-4)^2$
19.	a. 3 b. 0 c. -6
20.	a. $x^2-2x-15$ b. x^2-49 c. $x^2+4xy+4y^2$
21.	a. $(x+2)(x+5)$ b. $(x+y)(x-y)$ c. $\left(y-6\right)^2$
22.	a. 4 b. -5 c. -12
23.	$4\left(x^2+4x+3\right) \rightarrow 4x^2+16x+12$
24.	When you distribute the 4 to both binomials, the result is 4 times larger than it should be.
25.	$-2\left(x^2-4x-5\right) \rightarrow -2x^2+8x+10$
26.	a. -2 b. -3 c. -3
27.	Neither; $2(x-6)(x+1)$ is correct.
28.	a. $(x+2)(x+5)$ b. $(x+7)(x+1)$ c. $(x+4)(x+31)$

29.	a. $(x-2)(x+9)$ b. $(x-6)(x+1)$ c. $(x-5)(x+32)$
30.	a. $(x+2)(x+1)$ b. $(x-2)(x-1)$ c. $(x-2)(x+1)$ d. $(x+2)(x-1)$
31.	a. $4x\left(x-5\right)$ b. $-3\left(2x^2-6x+1\right)$ c. $7x\left(2x^2-x-5\right)$
32.	a. $(x-12)(x-1)$ b. $(x-3)(x-8)$ c. $(x-40)(x-15)$
33.	a. $(x+7)(x-1)$ b. $100(x+7)(x-1)$
34.	a. $x^3(x+7)(x-1)$ b. $-2(x+7)(x-1)$ c. $-3(x+7)(x-1)$
35.	a. $2(x+3)(x-1)$ b. $-3(x+5)(x+2)$
36.	$(3x+7)(x-1)$
37.	a. 3; $3x^2-x+1$ b. 1; x^2+2x-9 c. -1; $-x^2-8x+3$
38.	a. $(2x+1)(x+5)$ b. $(x+5)(3x+1)$ c. $(2x+5)(2x-3)$
39.	a. -1 b. -22 c. 8
40.	a. $(3x-2)(x+3)$ b. $(2x-7)(2x-1)$ c. $-(5x-3)(x+4)$ or $(-5x+3)(x+4)$
41.	a. $(2x+3)(x-2)$ b. $10(2x+3)(x-2)$
42.	a. $x(2x+3)(x-2)$ b. $-3(2x+3)(x-2)$ c. $-5(2x+3)(x-2)$
43.	The last term would need to be "+6".
44.	If you factor out the GCF first, you end up with $2(x-2)(x+10)$.
45.	a. $(x+2)(x-2)$ b. $(x+3)(x-3)$ c. $(4+x)(4-x)$
46.	a. $(5+x)(5-x)$ b. $(x+7)(x-7)$ c. $(9+x)(9-x)$
47.	a. $(x+10)(x-10)$ b. $(y+5)(y-5)$ c. $(m+20)(m-20)$
48.	a. $2(x+2)(x-2)$ b. $2(x+3)(x-3)$ c. $3(4+x)(4-x)$
49.	a. $3(5+x)(5-x)$ b. $x(x+7)(x-7)$ c. $-2(x-6)(x+6)$
50.	It cannot be factored. It is prime.
51.	a. $(2x+7)(2x-7)$ b. $(4x+5y)(4x-5y)$
52.	a. $(x^2+9)(x+3)(x-3)$ b. $(x^2+1)(x+1)(x-1)$
53.	$(x^4+1)(x^2+1)(x+1)(x-1)$
54.	a. $(x+1)^2$ b. $(x-2)^2$ c. $(x-3)^2$
55.	a. $(2x+5)^2$ b. $(1-5x)^2$ or $(5x-1)^2$ c. $9(2-x)^2$ or $9(x-2)^2$
56.	The factored form of each trinomial

	contains a binomial that is squared.
57.	a. $(y-x)^2$ b. $(2x-7y)^2$
58.	a. $2(x-7)^2$ b. $-x(x+9)^2$ c. $-(x-5y)^2$
59.	$A^2 + 2AB + B^2$
60.	$A^2 - 2AB + B^2$
61.	$(A-10B)^2$
62.	$x \cdot x$ is not $2x^2$
63.	If you factor out the GCF first, it becomes $x(x-9)(x+2)$.
64.	Both are correct
65.	a. $(A+B)^2$ b. $(A-B)^2$ c. $(3x-5)^2$
66.	In a perfect square trinomial, the middle term is twice the product of the square roots of the first and third terms. Stated another way, find the product of the first and third terms. Take the square root of that result. If the middle term is twice the value of that square root, the trinomial is a perfect square trinomial.
67.	6 ft; In the equation, replace t with 0.
68.	You could solve the equation $0=-16t^2+20t+6$, but you do not know how to do this yet. This is intentional. In the coming scenarios, you will learn how to solve this type of equation.
69.	–
70.	$(x+3)(x+2)$
71.	$x = -3$ or $x = -2$
72.	a. $x-3=0;\ x-4=0$ b. $x+2=0;\ x+5=0$ c. $3x-1=0;\ 2x+3=0$
73.	0
74.	$A = 0, B = -3$ or $A = 3, B = 0$
75.	a. 1 b. –1 c. 7 d. –3
76.	a. 1 b. –2 c. –5
77.	Each equation has 2 solutions. a. $x = 2$ or -3 b. $x = -7$ or 1 c. $x = 4$ or 5
78.	If the product of two factors is 0, then one of the factors must be zero.
79.	There are infinitely many options. $A=1, B=1$ or $A=2, B=\dfrac{1}{2}$ or $A=3, B=\dfrac{1}{3}$ or $A=4, B=\dfrac{1}{4}$ etc...
80.	$x = 3$ or -2 but neither one makes the original equation true.
81.	#2; The product equals "0," which forces one of the factors to be "0."
82.	a. $x=-3$ or -1 b. $x=-6$ or -4 c. $x=8$ or -2

83.	a. $x=-3$ or -1 b. $x=-6$ or -4 c. $x=8$ or -2
84.	$x = 5$ or 2
85.	$x = 10$ or -7
86.	$x = 6$
87.	$x = 5$ or 2
88.	a. 2 b. -2 c. $\dfrac{1}{4}$ d. $-\dfrac{3}{5}$
89.	a. $\dfrac{2}{3}$ b. $-\dfrac{1}{6}$ c. $\dfrac{5}{2}$
90.	a. $x=\dfrac{1}{6}, \dfrac{1}{2}$ b. $x=-\dfrac{2}{3}, \dfrac{2}{3}$ c. $x=-\dfrac{4}{3}, \dfrac{1}{5}$
91.	a. $x=\dfrac{3}{2}, 2$ b. $x=\dfrac{5}{2}$ c. $x=1, -\dfrac{5}{3}$
92.	a. $x=\dfrac{3}{2}, 2$ b. $x=\dfrac{5}{2}$ c. $x=1, -\dfrac{5}{3}$
93.	$(5x+1)(x-2)=0 \rightarrow x=-\dfrac{1}{5}$ or 2
94.	$(5x-2)(5x-2)=0 \rightarrow x=\dfrac{2}{5}$
95.	$(3x-2)(2x+5)=0 \rightarrow x=\dfrac{2}{3}$ or $-\dfrac{5}{2}$
96.	a. $x = 0, 4$ b. $x = 0, -7$ c. $x=0, \dfrac{1}{4}$
97.	The factor multiplied by the expression in parentheses can be replaced with 0 to make the equation true.
98.	a. $x = 0, 8$ b. $x = 0, -3$ c. $x = 0, 6$
99.	a. $x = 0, -9$ b. $x = 0, 10$ c. $x = 0, 2, -2$
100.	a. $x = 0, 3$ vs. $x = 3$ b. $x = 0, 6, 2$ vs. $x = 6, 2$ When you divide both sides by x, you "lose" the ability to see that $x = 0$ is one of the solutions.
101.	Distribute the "x" first and then make the equation equal 0. $x^2-4x=5 \rightarrow x^2-4x-5=0$
102.	a. $x = 0, 2, 3$ b. $x = 0, 5, -5$
103.	a. $-6(x^2-9x-10)=0$ $-6(x-10)(x+1)=0 \rightarrow x = 10, -1$ b. $-9(x^2-4)=0 \rightarrow -9(x+2)(x-2)=0$ $x = 2, -2$
104.	a. $0=-2(8t^2-10t-3)$ $0=-2(4t+1)(2t-3) \rightarrow t = -0.25$ or 1.5 b. $(n+2)(n+2)=324 \rightarrow n^2+4n+4=324$ $n^2+4n-320=0 \rightarrow (n+20)(n-16)=0$

	$n = -20$ or 16
105.	$x^2+5x+6=2 \rightarrow x^2+5x+4=0$ $(x+4)(x+1)=0 \rightarrow x = -1$ or -4
106.	No. The equation must equal 0 before you factor the expression. $x=-\dfrac{2}{3}, -4$
107.	$8x^2+2x-1=14 \rightarrow 8x^2+2x-15=0$ $(4x-5)(2x+3)=0 \rightarrow x = \dfrac{5}{4}, -\dfrac{3}{2}$
108.	$2x^2-2x=12 \rightarrow 2x^2-2x-12=0$ $2(x-3)(x+2) \rightarrow x = 3$ or -2
109.	$x = 0, 1$
110.	$x^2+10x+24=48 \rightarrow x^2+10x-24=0$ $(x+12)(x-2)=0 \rightarrow x=-12$ or 2 A rectangle cannot have negative side lengths. The only x-value that makes the sides have positive lengths is $x = 2$. Even though the equation has 2 solutions, one of the solutions can be ignored.
111.	a. 36 feet b. 3 seconds c. $\dfrac{1}{2}$ and $2\dfrac{3}{8}$ seconds
112.	a. $x = 3$ b. 22 cm
113.	1.5 x 6.5 solve: $x(x+5)=\dfrac{39}{4} \rightarrow x^2+5x=\dfrac{39}{4} \rightarrow$ $4x^2+20x-39=0 \rightarrow (2x-3)(2x+13)=0$ $x = 1.5$ or -6.5
114.	7in x 15in; solve $w(w+8)=105$; $w = 7$ or -15
115.	base: 10 cm; solve $\dfrac{1}{2}(x+5)(x+2)=35$; $x=5$
116.	base = 4.5cm; height = 4cm $\dfrac{1}{2}(x)(2x-5)=9 \rightarrow 2x^2-5x=18$ $2x^2-5x-18=0 \rightarrow (2x-9)(x+2)$ $x = 4.5$ or -2
117.	a. 26 b. $(n+1)^2+1$ or $n(n+2)+2$ or n^2+2n+2 c. 10th Figure; solve $n^2+2n+2=122$
118.	a. $x = 9$ b. $x = 23$ c. $x = 18$
119.	a. $x = 0, 8$ b. $x = 0, 5, -5$ c. $x=\dfrac{5}{3}, -1$
120.	Circle the equation in part a, b, and c.
121.	$x^2+5x+6=0$
122.	$x = 2$; solve $(2x-1)(3x+1) - (x-2)(x+1) = 21$

123.	a. $\dfrac{1}{2}$ b. $\dfrac{2}{5}$ b. $\dfrac{2}{5}$ b. $\dfrac{1}{4}$
124.	a. $\dfrac{2}{3}$ b. $\dfrac{x+5}{x+3}$ c. $\dfrac{3(x+2)}{5(x+2)} \rightarrow \dfrac{3}{5}$
125.	$\dfrac{(x+2)(x+1)}{(x+2)(x+4)} \rightarrow \dfrac{x+1}{x+4}$
126.	a. $\dfrac{(x+3)(x-3)}{(x+3)(x-5)} \rightarrow \dfrac{x-3}{x-5}$ b. $\dfrac{3(x^2-4)}{(x+9)(x-2)} \rightarrow \dfrac{3(x+2)(x-2)}{(x+9)(x-2)} \rightarrow \dfrac{3(x+2)}{x+9}$
127.	$\dfrac{2(4x^2-12x+9)}{2(2x^2+5x-12)} \rightarrow \dfrac{(2x-3)(2x-3)}{(2x-3)(2x+4)} \rightarrow \dfrac{2x-3}{x+4}$
128.	
129.	
130.	
131.	a. 2 x-values: 1 and −3 b. $y = 5$ c. No point has a y-value of −5
132.	a. $x=\dfrac{5}{2}, 2$ b. $x=\dfrac{7}{2}, 1$
133.	a. $(0, 2), (-3.5, 0)$ b. $\left(0, 5\right), \left(-\dfrac{1}{2}, 0\right), \left(\dfrac{5}{3}, 0\right)$
134.	a. $(0, -9)$, no x-intercept b. $(0, 25), (2.5, 0)$

43

135.	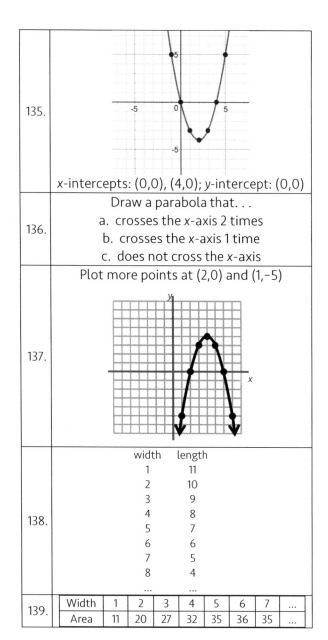 x-intercepts: (0,0), (4,0); y-intercept: (0,0)
136.	Draw a parabola that. . . a. crosses the x-axis 2 times b. crosses the x-axis 1 time c. does not cross the x-axis
137.	Plot more points at (2,0) and (1,−5)
138.	width length 1 11 2 10 3 9 4 8 5 7 6 6 7 5 8 4 ... ...

139.	Width	1	2	3	4	5	6	7	...
	Area	11	20	27	32	35	36	35	...

140.	
141.	a. $l = 7.5$ inches; $A = 33.75$ in^2 b. length: $12 - w$ c. Area: $w(12 - w)$
142.	a. $\dfrac{5x^3}{6}$ b. $9x^{16}$ c. $\dfrac{8}{a^{15}b^6}$
143.	a. $4x + 24$ b. $4x + 20$
144.	≤102 miles; solve $0.25 + .095m \le 10$
145.	\$812.00; solve $x + .0.07x = 868.84$
146.	a. $2 = x$ b. $x = \dfrac{4}{3}$
147.	a. Multiply both sides by $\dfrac{5}{3}$ b. Multiply both sides by $-\dfrac{3}{2}$
148.	a. $y = \dfrac{2}{5}x$ b. $y = -\dfrac{3}{2}x - 2$
149.	a. $y = 5$ b. $x = -2$
150.	(−2, 5)

SummitMath

Learn at your **own** pace.

Factoring Polynomials

Student-centered. Teacher-guided.

Review multiplying polynomials

1. The following multiplication scenarios are typically challenging. Work through each one as quickly as you can. Accuracy is more important than speed, though.

    a. 9×7 b. 7×4 c. 8×9 d. 7×8 e. 6×9 f. 7×6

2. Write down the entire prime factorization for each number shown.

    a. 32   b. 36

3. Write the prime factorization for each number.

    a. 48   b. 56   c. 63

4. The number 20 has the following <u>positive</u> factor pairs. Note: factor pairs must <u>only be</u> integers.

    $1 \times$ __ , $2 \times$ __ , $3 \times$ __ , and $4 \times$ __

5. Write down the <u>positive</u> factor pairs for each number shown below.

    a. 32   b. 36

6. Write down the <u>positive</u> factor pairs for each number.

    a. 48   b. 56   c. 63

7. Multiply each expression.

    a. $2x(x-1)$ b. $-5x(3x-2)$ c. $-x(3x^2-2x+1)$

8. Rewrite each expression as the product of a monomial and a binomial.

    a. $4B^2 + 24B$ b. $32x^2 - 24x$

9. In the previous scenario, how can you be sure that your product is a correctly rewritten form of the original expression?

10. Draw a rectangle that has the following area. Label the length of the base and height.

    a. $13x + 26$ b. $20x^2 + 5x + 10$

11. Multiply each expression.

    a. $(x+7)(x+2)$ b. $(x+6)(x-6)$ c. $(x+4)^2$

12. Simplify the expression as much as you can.

$$(x+3)(x^2 - 3x + 9)$$

Factoring out a greatest common factor

As a reminder, when you rewrite an expression as the product of two other expressions, the two expressions are called factors. In this sense, the word *factor* can be a noun. Furthermore, the process of rewriting an expression as a product of its factors is often referred to as factoring. In this sense, then, the word *factor* can be a verb.

13. Now that we have defined some new vocabulary, factor the following polynomials.

    a. $3x - 15$ b. $14x^2 + 6x - 10$

14. Factor each polynomial.

    a. $6x^2 + 12x + 27$ b. $12x^4 - 30x^3 - 24x^2$

Identifying a common factor can lead to different opinions. Consider the polynomial $12x^4 - 30x^3 - 24x^2$. The three terms of this trinomial share 2 as a common factor, as well as 3, 6, x, x^2, $6x$, and $6x^2$. In scenarios like this, it is typical to identify $6x^2$ as the greatest common factor (GCF).

15. The terms in the expression below have many factors in common. Identify all of the common factors of the terms in each expression.

    a. $24x^3 - 12x^2 + 20$ b. $6x^2 + 12x^3$

16. Identify the <u>greatest</u> common factor of each expression in the previous scenario.

17. Factor each trinomial.

    a. $30x^6 - 60x^3 - 45x^5$ b. $20x^3 + 30x^4 - 28x^2$

18. Multiply the following binomials. Notice how the terms in the result are related to the terms in the original binomials.

    a. $(x+5)(x+6)$ b. $(x-5)(x+5)$ c. $(x-4)^2$

In an earlier scenario, the factored form of polynomial was the product of a monomial and a trinomial. In the previous scenario, the factored form is the product of two binomials. Some polynomials cannot be factored at all, such as x^2+2x+5.

19. Look at your work for the 3 multiplication scenarios in the previous scenario. Could you do that work in reverse? In other words, if you started with your final expression, could you work backwards to figure out the two binomials that you multiplied to produce that expression? Try to do that with the following expressions. Write each expression as the product of two binomials.

    a. x^2+5x+6 b. $x^2+7x+12$ c. $x^2+10x+16$

20. Write each expression as the product of two binomials.

    a. x^2-x-6 b. $x^2-4x-12$ c. $x^2+15x-16$

21. What value of T will make the two expressions equivalent?

    a. $x^2+Tx-20$ and $(x-2)(x+10)$

    b. $x^2+Tx-64$ and $(x+8)(x-8)$

    c. $x^2+Txy+16y^2$ and $(x+4y)^2$

22. Once again, multiply the following binomials and try to make connections between the terms in your final expression and the original binomials that you multiplied.

    a. $(x+9)(x-1)$ b. $(x-9y)(x+9y)$ c. $(x-7y)^2$

23. Once again, try to work backwards to write each expression as the product of two binomials.

   a. $x^2 + 12x + 11$ b. $x^2 - 36$ c. $x^2 + 20xy + 100y^2$

The single most important mental activity involved in factoring is the process of multiplying your factors together to check your answer. You will also find that it helps to start out by *trying* to factor out a GCF from the entire expression. You may not be *able* to factor out a GCF, but if you can, it may help you find additional factors more easily.

24. Fill in the blank to make each expression equal to the factors written below the expression.

   a.
   $x^2 + \underline{\quad} x + 18$
   $(x-9)(x-2)$

   b.
   $x^2 + \underline{\quad} x - 25$
   $(x+5)(x-5)$

   c.
   $x^2 - 7x + 12$
   $(x + \underline{\quad})(x-4)$

25. Multiply the expressions below to create an equivalent expression without parentheses.

   $10(x+2)(x+5)$

26. When you try to multiply the expressions below, it may be confusing to know how to proceed with the "10" to the left of the first binomial. You may find it easier to first multiply the binomials before distributing the "10", but you can also start by distributing the "10" to the first binomial. Try a third option. Distribute the "10" to both of the binomials and then multiply the binomials. Write down your simplified result to see if it matches the other two options.

27. Multiply the expressions below to find an equivalent expression without parentheses.

   $-4(x+3)(x-2)$

28. Fill in the blank to make each expression equal to the factors written below the expression.

   a.
   $2x^2 + \underline{\quad} x - 80$
   $2(x-8)(x+5)$

   b.
   $3x^2 + \underline{\quad} x - 24$
   $3(x+4)(x-2)$

   c.
   $-x^2 + 18x - 32$
   $-(x-2)(x + \underline{\quad})$

50

29. For the trinomial $-x^2 + 14x - 24$, which factorization is correct?

$$-(x-8)(x-3) \quad \text{or} \quad -(x-4)(x-6)$$

30. Each trinomial below has been factored but the plus or minus signs are missing. Fill in either a plus sign (+) or a minus sign (−) to make the factors correct.

a.
$x^2 - 33x + 200$
$(x \quad 25)(x \quad 8)$

b.
$x^2 + 73x - 150$
$(x \quad 2)(x \quad 75)$

c.
$x^2 + 29x + 100$
$(x \quad 4)(x \quad 25)$

31. Each trinomial below has been factored but some of the signs and numbers are missing. Fill in any missing details to make the factors correct.

a.
$x^2 + 16x + 39$
$(x \quad 13)(x \quad 3)$

b.
$x^2 - 8x + 7$
$(x \quad 1)(x \quad 7)$

c.
$x^2 - 5x - 126$
$(x \quad 9)(x \quad 14)$

32. Factor the following trinomials.

a. $x^2 + 7x + 6$
b. $x^2 - 7x + 6$
c. $x^2 - x - 6$
d. $x^2 + x - 6$

33. Factor each polynomial below by writing it as the product of a monomial and a remaining polynomial. The monomial should be the greatest common factor of the original polynomial.

a. $-2x^2 + 6x$
b. $-2x^2 - 10x + 14$
c. $15x^4 - 35x^3 - 55x^2$

34. Factor the following trinomials. Check your answer by multiplying your factors together. By doing this, you will know if your factors are correct.

a. $x^2 - 5x - 6$
b. $20x^2 - 100x - 120$

The previous scenario is designed to show you that it helps to start out by *trying* to factor out a GCF from the entire expression. You may not be *able* to factor out a GCF, but if you can, it may help you find additional factors more easily.

35. Factor each trinomial below.

    a. $2x^6 - 10x^5 - 12x^4$ b. $-3x^2 + 15x + 18$ c. $-x^3 + 5x^2 + 6x$

36. Factor the following trinomials. Verify that your factors are correct.

    a. $3x^2 + 18x - 21$ b. $-5x^2 + 40x - 60$ c. $2x^2 - 7x - 9$

Factoring the trinomial in part c. in the previous scenario can be challenging. When you begin to learn about factoring, it is easier to find the factors of a trinomial when the leading coefficient is 1 (as in $1x^2$, or simply x^2). If the leading coefficient is any number <u>other than 1</u>, you need to pay close attention to that coefficient and check your factors to see if they are correct.

37. Identify the leading coefficient in each trinomial.

    a. $4x^2 - 3x - 7$ b. $2x^2 + 7x + 3$ c. $-x^2 - 3x + 4$

38. It may be helpful to go through the mental cycle of multiplying binomials one more time. Multiply the following binomials and try to make connections between the terms in your final expression and the original binomials that you multiplied.

    a. $(2x - 5)(x + 2)$ b. $(3x + 7)(x - 1)$ c. $(3x - 1)(2x + 3)$

39. Fill in the blank to make each expression equal to the factors written below the expression.

    a. $2x^2 + \underline{\quad}x - 7$
        $(2x + 7)(x - 1)$

    b. $3x^2 + \underline{\quad}x - 10$
        $(3x + 2)(x - 5)$

    c. $4x^2 + \underline{\quad}x - 7$
        $(2x - 1)(2x + 7)$

40. Fill in the blank to make each expression equal to the factors written below the expression.

    a. $3x^2 - 5x - 2$
        $(\underline{\quad} + 1)(\underline{\quad} - 2)$

    b. $5x^2 - 13x - 6$
        $(\underline{\quad} - 3)(\underline{\quad} + 2)$

    c. $6x^2 - 7x - 3$
        $(\underline{\quad} + 1)(\underline{\quad} - 3)$

41. What value of U will make the two expressions equivalent?

    a. $3x^2 + Ux - 24$ and $(3x - 8)(x + 3)$

    b. $5x^2 + Ux - 15$ and $(x + 5)(5x - 3)$

    c. $12x^2 + Ux - 3$ and $(6x + 1)(2x - 3)$

42. Rewrite each trinomial in Standard Form and identify the leading coefficient in that trinomial.

    a. $1 + 5x^2 - 6x$ b. $9x + 7 + 2x^2$ c. $3 - 8x - x^2$

43. Factor the previous three trinomials. Check your result by multiplying your factors together.

44. Factor the following trinomials. Check your result by multiplying your factors together.

    a. $4x^2 - 7 - 3x$ b. $3 + 2x^2 + 7x$ c. $-3x + 4 - x^2$

45. Factor the following trinomials. Check your result by multiplying your factors together.

    a. $5x^2 - 6 + 7x$ b. $6x^2 - 17x + 10$ c. $-x^2 + 12x - 36$

At this point, there isn't much more to learn about factoring. In order to strengthen your long-term understanding of this topic, though, we will continue to look more closely at factoring and try to sort out some of the patterns that may help you factor expressions more quickly.

46. Factor the following trinomials.

  a. $15 - 11x + 2x^2$

  b. $30 - 22x + 4x^2$

Once again, the previous scenario is designed to show you that it helps to start out by *trying* to factor out a GCF from the entire expression.

47. Factor each trinomial below.

  a. $-15x + 11x^2 - 2x^3$

  b. $20x^2 - 110x + 150$

  c. $-6x^2 + 33x - 45$

48. Explain why $(2x - 1)(2x - 6)$ cannot be the factorization of $4x^2 - 12x + 6$.

Factoring a difference of two squares

49. Factor the following expressions. Check your answer by multiplying your factors together.

    a. $x^2+0x-36$ b. $x^2+0x-49$ c. $64+0x-x^2$

50. Factor the following expressions. Check your answer by multiplying your factors together.

    a. $81+0x-x^2$ b. x^2-100 c. $121-x^2$

51. Factor the following expressions. Why are they more difficult than the ones in the previous scenario?

    a. $-3x^2+27$ b. $-x^4+x^2$

52. Factor the following expressions. Check your answer by multiplying your factors together.

    a. $6x^2-24$ b. $24-6x^2$ c. $-5x^2+45$

53. Factor each expression. Check your answer by multiplying your factors together.

    a. $810-10x^2$ b. $64x-x^3$ c. $-2x^3+98x$

54. Factor the following expressions.

    a. $36x^2-121$ b. x^2-144y^2 c. x^2-16

Many of the previous polynomials (sometimes after factoring out a GCF) have a form of $A^2 - B^2$. This form is known as the difference of two squares. When you identify this form, it will always factor quickly into the following two binomials: $(A + B)(A - B)$.

55. Factor the expression $x^4 - 16$.

56. Factor the expression $16x^4 - 1$.

57. If $x^2 - y^2$ can be factored as $(x+y)(x-y)$, how can $x^2 + y^2$ be factored?

Factoring perfect square trinomials

58. Factor the following trinomials. Check your answer by multiplying your factors together. What pattern do you notice?

    a. $x^2 - 2x + 1$ b. $x^2 - 12x + 36$ c. $x^2 + 14x + 49$

59. Factor the following trinomials. Check your answer by multiplying your factors together. What pattern do you notice?

    a. $4x^2 + 4x + 1$ b. $25x^2 + 70x + 49$ c. $x^2 + x + \dfrac{1}{4}$

60. Factor the following trinomials.

    a. $x^2 + \dfrac{2}{3}x + \dfrac{1}{9}$ b. $x^2 + \dfrac{4}{5}x + \dfrac{4}{25}$ c. $x^2 + \dfrac{7}{5}x + \dfrac{49}{100}$

61. Factor the following trinomials.

    a. $12x - 3x^2 - 12$ b. $64x + x^3 - 16x^2$ c. $4xy - 4y^2 - x^2$

When you factor the previous groups of trinomials, they each involve a trinomial that has a repeated factor. Just as $49P^2$ is a perfect square because it can be written as $(7P)^2$, these trinomials are called perfect square trinomials.

62. One type of perfect square trinomial will always factor into $(F+G)(F+G)$ or $(F+G)^2$. Multiply these factors back together to see the original trinomial.

63. A perfect square trinomial may also sometimes factor into $(C-D)(C-D)$ or $(C-D)^2$. Multiply these factors back together to see the original trinomial.

64. Factor the expression $M^2 - 16MN + 64N^2$.

65. Explain why $(4x-7)(x-5)$ cannot be the factorization of $4x^2 - 20x + 35$.

66. Factor the following trinomials.

    a. $x^2 + 2xy + y^2$ b. $4x^2 - 12xy + 9y^2$ c. $25x^2 - 100x + 100$

67. Explain how to determine if a trinomial is a perfect square trinomial.

Using factoring to solve equations

Consider some scenarios that involve polynomials like the ones you have been working with so far.

68. A diver stands at the top of a cliff looking down on a deep lake below. When the diver jumps, her path through the air is modeled by the equation $H = -16t^2 + 64$, where H is the height of the diver, in feet, t seconds after she jumps. What is the height of the diver at the exact moment she jumps?

69. In the previous scenario, how long is the diver in the air before she hits the water?

When the diver hits the water, her height is 0. In the equation $H = -16t^2 + 64$, if you replace H with 0, the equation becomes $0 = -16t^2 + 64$. You can try to isolate "t" in this equation, but you may not know how to solve this type of equation yet.

For now, consider the next scenario, which will begin to show you how to solve a new type of equation. As you become more familiar with solving this type of equation, you may be able to come back and answer the question in the previous scenario.

70. What x-value makes each equation true?

    a. $0 = x + 2$ b. $x - 3 = 0$ c. $0 = x + 4$

71. What x-value makes each equation true?

    a. $5(x - 3) = 0$ b. $-2(x + 1) = 0$ c. $-3(x - 7) = 0$

72. What values of x will make each equation true?

    a. $(x - 6)(x + 1) = 0$ b. $(x - 10)(x - 9) = 0$ c. $(x + 8)(x + 11) = 0$

73. In the scenarios above, the factors have a product of 0. Why does this make it possible to determine values of x that will make each equation true?

74. Solve the following equations.

    a. $x^2+7x+10=0$
    b. $x^2-8x+15=0$
    c. $x^2+x-20=0$

75. The equation $(F)(G)=0$ is true if $F=0$. It is also true if $G=0$. Suppose, instead that $(F)(G)=2$. What values of F and G make this statement true?

76. Solve the equation $(x+3)(x+4)=3$ by setting both factors equal to 3. Check your solutions to see if either one makes the original equation true.

77. Which equation is easier to solve? Why is this?

    Equation 1: $(x+3)(x+4)=3$
    Equation 2: $(x+3)(x+4)=0$

78. It is difficult to find values of x that make Equation 1 true in the previous scenario. It will become easier to solve, though, if you can find a way to change the equation. Try to change Equation 1 to make it look more like Equation 2 in the previous scenario.

79. Solve the equation $(x-2)(x+6)=9$.

80. What x-value makes each equation true?

    a. $5x+3=0$
    b. $7x-1=0$

81. Solve each equation.

    a. $2(5x+3)=0$ b. $10(7x-1)=0$

82. What values of x will make each equation true?

    a. $(4x-1)(x-5)=0$ b. $(x+8)(8x-1)=0$ c. $(3x+2)(4x-5)=0$

83. Solve the following equations.

    a. $10=6x^2+28x$ b. $20x^2-45=0$ c. $9x^2+4=12x$

84. What values of x will make each equation true?

    a. $x(x-2)=0$ b. $x(x+3)=0$ c. $5x(2x+3)=0$

85. In each of the previous three equations, one of the solutions is 0. Why does this occur?

86. Solve the following equations.

    a. $x^2+2x=0$ b. $x^2-3x+5=5$ c. $3=10x^2-15x+3$

87. What values of x will make each equation true?

    a. $x^3(x-11)=0$
    b. $7x^2(x+4)=0$
    ★c. $2x(x^2-1)=0$

88. Solve the following equations in two different ways. For the first approach, factor as you have learned to do in the previous scenarios. For the second approach, divide both sides by x and then proceed with factoring. What do you notice?

    a. $x^2=10x$
    b. $x^3-2x^2+x=0$

89. Solve the following equations.

    a. $4x^2-21x+5=0$
    b. $8x^2+63x-8=0$
    c. $12x^2-7x-10=0$

90. In a previous scenario, you saw the equation below, but you may not have known how to solve it. Try to solve it now.

$$-16t^2+64=0$$

91. Solve the equation $(x-6)(x-1)=14$. Check your solutions.

92. Solve the equation $\dfrac{1}{6}x^2-\dfrac{1}{3}x-\dfrac{1}{2}=0$.

93. The fractions in the previous equation make it challenging. Consider another equation with fractions:

$\frac{1}{8}x = \frac{1}{2}$. How can you alter this equation to make it easier to solve?

94. Solve the equation by multiplying both sides by a value that will eliminate the fractions.

$$\frac{1}{6}x - \frac{2}{3} = \frac{1}{2}$$

95. Solve each equation by multiplying both sides by a value that will eliminate the fractions. Try to find the smallest value that will do this, to keep the numbers as small possible.

a. $\frac{1}{4}x^2 - \frac{5}{4}x + 1 = 0$ ★b. $x^2 - 7x + 8.25 = 0$

96. Solve the equation below.

$$x^3 - 2x^2 = 15x$$

97. Fill in the blank. To solve the equation below, it would be helpful to first multiply both sides by the number _____ to clear all of the fractions on both sides. Do not solve the equation.

$$\frac{2x}{5} - 1 = \frac{1}{3}x - \frac{5}{6}$$

98. Solve the previous equation.

99. A bug sits on a leaf of a plant and gets ready to jump down into a puddle on the ground. A frog waits patiently on the ground. When the bug jumps, its path is modeled by the equation $H = -16t^2 + 2t + 4$. In the equation, H is the height of the frog in inches and t is the time that has passed after the bug jumps, measured in seconds. If the frog wants to catch the bug with its tongue when the bug is 1 inch above the ground, how long will the frog need to wait after the bug jumps to extend its tongue? Assume the frog catches the bug at the exact moment that it reaches out its tongue.

100. The area of the rectangle shown is 12 in².

    a. What is the value of x?

    b. What is the perimeter of the rectangle?

101. Rabbits and deer like to eat the plants in your garden, so you buy enough fencing to surround your rectangular garden. The area of the rectangle that you can surround with fencing is modeled by the equation $A = w(40 - w)$, where A is the area of the rectangle if it has a width of w feet.

    a. What is the area of the rectangle, if the width is 10 feet?

    b. How many feet of fencing do you need to buy if the width is 10 feet?

102. ★In the previous scenario, what is the width of the rectangle if the area is 357.75 square feet?

103. What is the perimeter of the outer rectangle if the shaded region has an area of 92 square units?

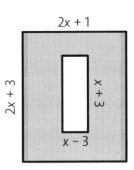

2x + 1

2x + 3

x + 3

x − 3

104. The area of a triangle is 20 square inches. Its height is 2 inches longer than twice the length of its base. What are the dimensions of the triangle?

105. Equations like 3x − 5 = 8 and −2x + 3 = x usually have one solution and they are known as <u>linear</u> equations. Solve the following linear equations.

    a. $3(x-6)=5x-4$ b. $1-3(2x-1)=19$

106. Equations like x^2 + 3x + 2 = 0 and x^2 + 5x = 6 are called <u>quadratic</u> equations and they can be rearranged to look like $Ax^2+Bx+C=0$. Solve the following equations.

    a. $(y-7)(y+2)=0$ b. $3y^2-7y=20$

Using factoring to simplify fractions

107. Simplify each of the following fractions.

    a. $\dfrac{2 \cdot 10}{3 \cdot 10}$
    b. $\dfrac{2 \cdot 3}{3 \cdot 5}$
    c. $\dfrac{3x}{8x}$
    d. $\dfrac{8y}{12y}$

108. Simplify each of the following fractions.

    a. $\dfrac{3x(x+4)}{5x(x+4)}$
    b. $\dfrac{(x+1)(x+3)}{(x+1)(x+7)}$
    c. $\dfrac{6x+6}{7x+7}$

109. In the previous scenario, the last fraction can only be simplified after you factor the expressions in the numerator and denominator. After you factor, it becomes clear that there are identical factors in the numerator and denominator. Use this strategy to simplify each of the following fractions.

$$\dfrac{x^2+4x+3}{x^2+8x+7}$$

110. Simplify each fraction by cancelling out disguised forms of 1.

    a. $\dfrac{x^2-1}{x^2+2x+1}$
    b. $\dfrac{x^2+6x+5}{x^2-25}$

111. Simplify the following fraction: $\dfrac{6x^2-27x-15}{9x^2-42x-15}$.

Introduction to graphing parabolas

112. If you graph every ordered pair for the equation $y = \frac{1}{2}x - 2$ what will be the shape of your graph? Draw the graph.

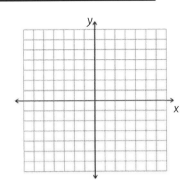

113. When you graph all of the ordered pairs represented by the equation $y = x^2 - 2$, the shape of the graph is. . . actually, let's see if you can figure out the shape of the graph. Use what you know about graphing equations to create a thorough graph of this equation.

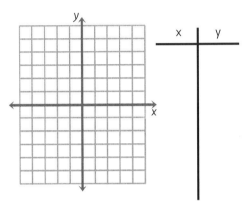

The graph in the previous scenario has a curved shape that makes it very different than linear graphs. In mathematics, there is a technical name for practically everything. This specially curved graph is called a parabola (puh-RA-buh-luh). Additionally, while the structure $y = \frac{1}{2}x - 2$ is called a linear equation, the structure $y = x^2 - 2$ is called a quadratic equation.

114. Graph the equation $y = -x^2 + 1$.

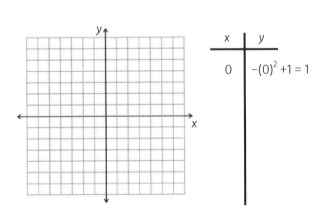

x	y
0	$-(0)^2 + 1 = 1$

115. Consider the parabola to the right.

   a. Determine the x-value(s) for which the parabola has a y-value of 0.

   b. Determine the y-value(s) for which the parabola has an x-value of 3.

   c. Determine the x-value(s) for which the parabola has a y-value of 6.

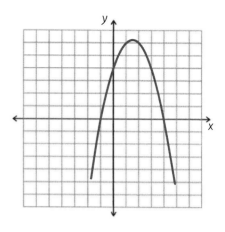

116. Determine the x-value(s) for which the equation $y=-x^2+3x+10$ has a y-value of

   a. 0

   ★b. 10

117. Identify any x- and y-intercepts for each of the following equations.

   a. $3x+2y=12$

   b. $y=x^2-2x-8$

118. ★Identify any x- and y-intercepts for each of the following equations.

   a. $x^2+y=3$

   b. $y=4x^2-12x+9$

119. ★Draw a very basic sketch of a parabola that has each of the following characteristics.

   a. no x-intercepts

   b. one x-intercept

   c. two x-intercepts

120. ★Identify the *x*- and *y*-intercepts of the following equation. Then, graph the equation to verify the accuracy of your intercepts.

$$y = x^2 - 2x - 3$$

121. Part of a parabola is shown below. Even though you do not have the equation for the parabola, use what you have learned so far to plot more points that are on the parabola. Use those points to finish drawing the parabola.

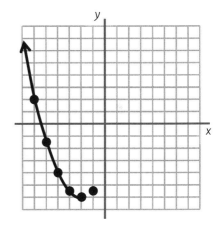

122. Simplify each expression by eliminating parentheses and using only positive exponents.

   a. $\dfrac{x^{-2}}{x^{-3}}$

   b. $\left(-\dfrac{1}{3}\right)^{-3}$

   c. $2\left(x^{-1}\right)^{2}$

123. The average (arithmetic mean) of 7, 13, 21, and H is 10. Determine the value of H.

124. Write the equation for both lines shown, in Slope-Intercept Form.

   a. Line 1

   b. Line 2

   c. Are the two lines perpendicular? How do you know?

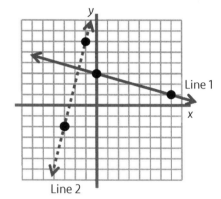

125. The average TV viewership for the Super Bowl from 2006 to 2015 (a 10-year period) was 104.3 million people. When you include the 2016 Super Bowl, the average viewership from 2006 to 2016 was 105 million people. How many people watched the 2016 Super Bowl?

126. Solve each equation.

   a. $7x-6=\dfrac{1}{3}\left(6x-3\right)$

   b. $-x+9=-\dfrac{1}{5}x+2$

127. If the slope of the line $y = 2 + 7x$ is changed to become -4, what is the new equation of the line?

128. What is the slope of the line $3x = 2(y - 6)$?

129. A parenting survey was conducted in 2015 in a local town to find out what challenges parents face as they raise their children. 60% of fathers in the town chose to take the survey, while 40% of mothers chose to take the survey.

    a. If 55% of the parents in the town are mothers, what percent of the parents in the entire town chose to take the survey?

    b. A total of 6,125 parents took the survey in 2015. What was the total number of parents in the town in 2015?

130. Circle the equations that are quadratic.

    a. $2x^2 - x = 6$ b. $2x - 6 = x$ c. $3x = 4 - x^2$

131. The two solutions to a quadratic equation have a sum of -7 and a product of 12. Write down the equation in the form $Ax^2 + Bx + C = 0$.

Homework|Extra Practice Answer Key

1.	a. 63 b. 28 c. 72 d. 56 e. 54 f. 42
2.	a. 2^5 b. $2^2 \times 3^2$
3.	a. $2^4 \times 3$ b. $2^3 \times 7$ c. $3^2 \times 7$
4.	20, 10, none, 5
5.	a. $1 \times 32, 2 \times 16, 4 \times 8$ b. $1 \times 36, 2 \times 18, 3 \times 12, 4 \times 9, 6 \times 6$
6.	a. $1 \times 48, 2 \times 24, 3 \times 16, 4 \times 12, 6 \times 8$ b. $1 \times 56, 2 \times 28, 4 \times 14, 7 \times 8$ c. $1 \times 63, 3 \times 21, 7 \times 9$
7.	a. $2x^2 - 2x$ b. $-15x^2 + 10x$ c. $-3x^3 + 2x^2 - x$
8.	a. $4B(B+6)$ b. $8x(4x-3)$
9.	Multiply the monomial and binomial to see if you get the original expression.
10.	13 $x + 2$ 5 $4x^2 + x + 2$
11.	a. $x^2 + 2x + 7x + 14 \rightarrow x^2 + 9x + 14$ b. $x^2 - 6x + 6x - 36 \rightarrow x^2 - 36$ c. $(x+4)(x+4) \rightarrow x^2 + 8x + 16$
12.	$x^3 - 3x^2 + 9x + 3x^2 - 9x + 27 \rightarrow x^3 + 27$
13.	a. $3(x-5)$ b. $2(7x^2 + 3x - 5)$
14.	a. $3(2x^2 + 4x + 9)$ b. $6x^2(2x^2 - 5x - 4)$
15.	a. 2, 4 b. 2, 3, 6, 2x, 3x, 6x, $2x^2$, $3x^2$, $6x^2$
16.	a. 4 b. $6x^2$
17.	a. $15x^3(2x^3 - 4 - 3x^2)$ b. $2x^2(10x + 15x^2 - 14)$
18.	a. $x^2 + 11x + 30$ b. $x^2 - 25$ c. $x^2 - 8x + 16$
19.	a. $(x+2)(x+3)$ b. $(x+3)(x+4)$ c. $(x+8)(x+2)$
20.	a. $(x-3)(x+2)$ b. $(x-6)(x+2)$ c. $(x+16)(x-1)$
21.	a. $T = 8$ b. $T = 0$ c. $T = 8$
22.	a. $x^2 + 8x - 9$ b. $x^2 - 81y^2$ c. $x^2 - 14xy + 49y^2$
23.	a. $(x+11)(x+1)$ b. $(x+6)(x-6)$ c. $(x+10y)(x+10y)$ or $(x+10y)^2$
24.	a. −11 b. 0 c. −3
25.	$10(x^2 + 7x + 10) \rightarrow 10x^2 + 70x + 100$
26.	$(10x+20)(10x+50) \rightarrow 100x^2 + 700x + 1000$ When you distribute the 10 to both binomials, the result is 10 times larger than it should be.
27.	$-4(x^2 + x - 6) \rightarrow -4x^2 - 4x + 24$
28.	a. −6 b. 6 c. −16
29.	Neither. It is $-(x-12)(x-2)$.
30.	a. $(x-25)(x-8)$ b. $(x-2)(x+75)$ c. $(x+4)(x+25)$
31.	a. $(x+13)(x+3)$ b. $(x-1)(x-7)$ c. $(x+9)(x-14)$
32.	a. $(x+6)(x+1)$ b. $(x-1)(x-6)$ c. $(x-3)(x+2)$ d. $(x+3)(x-2)$
33.	a. $-2x(x-3)$ or $2x(-x+3)$ b. $-2(x^2 + 5x - 7)$ or $2(-x^2 - 5x + 7)$ c. $5x^2(3x^2 - 7x - 11)$
34.	a. $(x-6)(x+1)$ b. $20(x-6)(x+1)$
35.	a. $2x^4(x-6)(x+1)$ b. $-3(x-6)(x+1)$ c. $-x(x-6)(x+1)$
36.	a. $3(x+7)(x-1)$ b. $-5(x-6)(x-2)$ c. $(2x-9)(x+1)$
37.	a. 4 b. 2 c. −1
38.	a. $2x^2 - x - 10$ b. $3x^2 + 4x - 7$ c. $6x^2 + 7x - 3$
39.	a. 5 b. −13 c. 12
40.	a. $(3x+1)(x-2)$ b. $(x-3)(5x+2)$ c. $(3x+1)(2x-3)$
41.	a. 1 b. 22 c. −16
42.	a. $5x^2 - 6x + 1$ b. $2x^2 + 9x + 7$ c. $-x^2 - 8x + 3$
43.	a. $(5x-1)(x-1)$ b. $(2x+7)(x+1)$ c. $(-x-3)(x-1)$ or $-(x+3)(x-1)$
44.	a. $(4x-7)(x+1)$ b. $(2x+1)(x+3)$ c. $-(x+4)(x-1)$ or $(-x-4)(x-1)$

	or $(x+4)(-x+1)$
45.	a. $(5x-3)(x+2)$ b. $(6x-5)(x-2)$ c. $-(x-6)(x-6)$ or $(-x+6)(x-6)$
46.	a. $(2x-5)(x-3)$ b. $2(2x-5)(x-3)$
47.	a. $-x(2x-5)(x-3)$ b. $10(2x-5)(x-3)$ c. $-3(2x-5)(x-3)$
48.	$(2x-1)(2x-6) = 4x^2-14x+6$
49.	a. $(x+6)(x-6)$ b. $(x+7)(x-7)$ c. $(8+x)(8-x)$
50.	a. $(9+x)(9-x)$ b. $(x+10)(x-10)$ c. $(11+x)(11-x)$
51.	These are more difficult because they have a greatest common factor that can be factored out first. a. $-3(x+3)(x-3)$ b. $-x^2(x+1)(x-1)$
52.	a. $6(x+2)(x-2)$ b. $6(2+x)(2-x)$ c. $-5(x+3)(x-3)$
53.	a. $10(9+x)(9-x)$ b. $x(8+x)(8-x)$ c. $-2x(x+7)(x-7)$
54.	a. $(6x+11)(6x-11)$ b. $(x+12y)(x-12y)$ c. $(x+4)(x-4)$
55.	$(x^2+4)(x^2-4)\to(x^2+4)(x+2)(x-2)$
56.	$(4x^2+1)(2x+1)(2x-1)$
57.	It cannot be factored
58.	a. $(x-1)^2$ b. $(x-6)^2$ c. $(x+7)^2$
59.	a. $(2x+1)^2$ b. $(5x+7)^2$ c. $\left(x+\dfrac{1}{2}\right)^2$
60.	a. $\left(x+\dfrac{1}{3}\right)^2$ b. $\left(x+\dfrac{2}{5}\right)^2$ c. $\left(x+\dfrac{7}{10}\right)^2$
61.	a. $-3(x-2)^2$ b. $x(x-8)^2$ c. $-(x-2y)^2$
62.	$F^2+2FG+G^2$
63.	$C^2-2CD+D^2$
64.	$(M-8N)^2$
65.	$(4x-7)(x-5)=4x^2-27x+35$
66.	a. $(x+y)^2$ b. $(2x-3y)^2$ c. $25(x-2)^2$
67.	In a perfect square trinomial, the middle

	term is twice the product of the square roots of the first and third terms. Stated another way, find the product of the first and third terms. Take the square root of that result. If the middle term is twice the value of that square root, the trinomial is a perfect square trinomial.
68.	64 feet (Let $t = 0$.)
69.	2 sec; Let $H = 0$. Solve $0=-16t^2+64$.
70.	a. $x = -2$ b. $x = 3$ c. $x = -4$
71.	a. $x = 3$ b. $x = -1$ c. $x = 7$
72.	a. $x = 6, -1$ b. $x = 10, 9$ c. $x = -8, -11$
73.	If the product of two factors is 0, one of the factors must be 0.
74.	a. $(x+2)(x+5)=0\to x=-2, -5$ b. $(x-3)(x-5)=0\to x=3, 5$ c. $(x+5)(x-4)=0\to x=4, -5$
75.	Infinitely many options; $F=2, G=1$ or $F=4, G=\dfrac{1}{2}$ or $F=6, G=\dfrac{1}{3}$ etc...
76.	$x = 0$ or -1 but neither one makes the original equation true.
77.	#2; The product equals "0," which forces one of the factors to be "0."
78.	$x = -2$ or -5 $x^2+7x+12=2\to x^2+7x+10=0$
79.	$x = -7, 3$
80.	a. $x=-\dfrac{3}{5}$ b. $x=\dfrac{1}{7}$
81.	a. $x=-\dfrac{3}{5}$ b. $x=\dfrac{1}{7}$
82.	a. $x=\dfrac{1}{4}, 5$ b. $x=-8, \dfrac{1}{8}$ c. $x=-\dfrac{2}{3}, \dfrac{5}{4}$
83.	a. $0=2(3x-1)(x+5)\to x=\dfrac{1}{3}, -5$ b. $5(2x+3)(2x-3)=0\to x=-\dfrac{3}{2}, \dfrac{3}{2}$ c. $9x^2-12x+4=0\to(3x-2)^2=0\to x=\dfrac{2}{3}$
84.	a. $x=0, 2$ b. $x=0, -3$ c. $x=0, -\dfrac{3}{2}$
85.	The factor multiplied by the expression in parentheses can be replaced with 0 to make the equation true.
86.	a. $x=0, -2$ b. $x=0, 3$ c. $x=0, \dfrac{3}{2}$
87.	a. $x=0, 11$ b. $x=0, -4$ c. $x=0, 1, -1$

88.	a. $x = 0,10$ vs. $x = 10$ b. $x = 0,1$ vs. $x = 1$ If you divide both sides by x, you will not see that $x = 0$ is one of the solutions.
89.	a. $(4x-1)(x-5)=0 \rightarrow x = \dfrac{1}{4}, 5$ b. $(8x-1)(x+8)=0 \rightarrow x = \dfrac{1}{8}, -8$ c. $(4x-5)(3x+2)=0 \rightarrow x = \dfrac{5}{4}, -\dfrac{2}{3}$
90.	a. $-16(t^2-4)=0 \rightarrow -16(t+2)(t-2)=0$ $t = 2, -2$
91.	$x^2-7x+6=14 \rightarrow x^2-7x-8=0$ $(x+1)(x-8)=0 \rightarrow x = 8, -1$
92.	$6\cdot\left(\dfrac{1}{6}x^2-\dfrac{1}{3}x-\dfrac{1}{2}\right)=0\cdot6 \rightarrow x^2-2x-3=0$ $(x-3)(x+1)=0 \rightarrow x = 3, -1$
93.	Multiply both sides by 8
94.	$6\cdot\left(\dfrac{1}{6}x-\dfrac{2}{3}\right)=\left(\dfrac{1}{2}\right)\cdot6 \rightarrow x-4=3 \rightarrow x = 7$
95.	a. $x = 4, 1$ b. $x = 5.5, 1.5$
96.	$x = 0, 5, -3$
97.	$30 \rightarrow$ least common multiple of 3, 5 and 6
98.	$30\cdot\left(\dfrac{2x}{5}-1\right)=\left(\dfrac{1}{3}x-\dfrac{5}{6}\right)\cdot30$ $\rightarrow 12x-30=10x-25 \rightarrow 2x=5 \rightarrow x = 2.5$
99.	One-half of a sec.; solve $1=-16t^2+2t+4$ $0=(8t+3)(2t-1) \rightarrow t = -\dfrac{3}{8}$ or $\dfrac{1}{2}$
100.	a. $x = 3$; Area $= b\cdot h$: solve $2x(x-1)=12$ b. $P =$ sum of all sides: $P = 16$ in.
101.	a. $300\ \text{ft}^2$ b. 80 feet
102.	$w = 13.5$ ft or 26.5 ft; solve: $w(40-w)=357.75 \rightarrow 4w-w^2=357.75$ $4\cdot(40w-w^2)=(357.75)\cdot4$ $160w-4w^2=1431 \rightarrow 0=4w^2-160w+1431$ $(2w-27)(2w-53)=0 \rightarrow w = 13.5$ or 26.5 ft
103.	perimeter: 40 units solve: $(2x+3)(2x+1)-(x+3)(x-3)=92$ $x = 4$
104.	base $= 4$ in.; height $= 10$ in. solve $\dfrac{1}{2}(x)(2x+2)=20 \rightarrow x^2+x=20$ $x^2+x-20=0 \rightarrow (x+5)(x-4)$ $x = 4$ or -5 (length can't be negative)

105.	a. $x = -7$ b. $x = -2.5$
106.	a. $y = 7, -2$ b. $3y^2-7y-20=0$ $\rightarrow (3y+5)(y-4)=0 \rightarrow y = -\dfrac{5}{3}, 4$
107.	a. $\dfrac{2}{3}$ b. $\dfrac{2}{5}$ c. $\dfrac{3}{8}$ d. $\dfrac{2}{3}$
108.	a. $\dfrac{3}{5}$ b. $\dfrac{x+3}{x+7}$ c. $\dfrac{6(x+1)}{7(x+1)} \rightarrow \dfrac{6}{7}$
109.	$\dfrac{(x+3)(x+1)}{(x+7)(x+1)} \rightarrow \dfrac{x+3}{x+7}$
110.	a. $\dfrac{(x+1)(x-1)}{(x+1)(x+1)} \rightarrow \dfrac{x-1}{x+1}$ b. $\dfrac{(x+5)(x+1)}{(x+5)(x-5)} \rightarrow \dfrac{x+1}{x-5}$
111.	$\dfrac{3(2x^2-9x-5)}{3(3x^2-14x-5)} \rightarrow \dfrac{3(2x+1)(x-5)}{(3x+1)(x-5)} \rightarrow \dfrac{2x+1}{3x+1}$
112.	
113.	
114.	
115.	a. $x = -1$ or 4 b. $y = 4$ c. $x = 1$ or 2
116.	a. $x = -2$ or 5; solve $0=-x^2+3x+10$ b. $x = 0$ or 3; solve $10=-x^2+3x+10$

74

117.	To find x-intercepts, replace y with 0. To find y-intercepts, replace x with 0. a. x-int: (4,0); y-int: (0,6) b. x-ints: (4,0) and (−2,0); y-int: (0,−8)
118.	a. x-ints: $\left(\sqrt{3},0\right)$ and $\left(-\sqrt{3},0\right)$; y-int: (0,3) b. x-int: (1.5,0); y-int: (0,9)
119.	Draw a parabola that. . . a. does not cross the x-axis b. crosses the x-axis 1 time c. crosses the x-axis 2 time2
120.	
121.	Plot points at (0,−4), (1,−1.5) and (2,2)

122.	a. x b. −27 c. $\dfrac{2}{x^2}$
123.	$H=-1$; solve $\dfrac{7+13+21+H}{4}=10$
124.	a. $y=-\dfrac{2}{7}x+3$ b. $y=4x+10$ c. No, the slopes need to be opposite reciprocals to make the lines perpendicular.
125.	112 million
126.	a. 1 b. 8.75
127.	$y=2-4x$ or $y=-4x+2$
128.	The slope of the line is $\dfrac{3}{2}$. $3x=2y-12\rightarrow 2y=3x+12\rightarrow y=\dfrac{3}{2}x+6$
129.	a. Suppose there are 100 in the town 55 mothers → .4(55) = 22 took survey 45 fathers → .6(45) = 27 took survey 49 took survey 49% of the parents took the survey b. 12,500 parents; solve: 6125 = 0.49x
130.	Circle the equations in parts a and c.
131.	$x=-3$ or $-4\rightarrow\left(x+3\right)\left(x+4\right)=0$ $\rightarrow x^2+7x+12=0$